Alone in the Storm

by Kathryn Snyder
illustrated by Karen Chandler

HOUGHTON MIFFLIN   BOSTON

Where Is Aunt Luelle?

Raylee looked out the window. The sky was gray. Far away, Raylee could see the ocean. She could see big waves. A storm was coming.

Last night, Raylee and her parents had heard on the radio that a storm was coming. They had put tape on the windows to keep them from breaking in the storm. But now the radio said the storm was a hurricane. Everyone was going to a shelter. Raylee was going to a shelter too. Aunt Luelle was coming to pick her up and they would go to the shelter together.

Momma called Raylee from her job. "I'll pick you up at noon," she said. "If I can't do it, Aunt Luelle will come. She will be there at one o'clock. We'll all meet at the shelter."

Momma didn't come at noon. At one o'clock it began to rain. The rain pounded against the windows. *Where is Aunt Luelle?* thought Raylee. *The dog and I are waiting.* Raylee looked around. Where was the dog? Where was Chomper?

Chomper did not like storms. Storms scared him. "Chomper!" called Raylee, "Chomper! Come here!"

Raylee looked all over the house. She looked under the beds. She looked in the closets. Then she looked outside. Chomper was sitting by the fence. Raylee called to the dog. But he wouldn't come. Raylee ran out into the rain. "Chomper! Come here!" she called. But Chomper was scared. He ran to the next house and hid under the porch.

Raylee found the dog twenty minutes later. She grabbed his collar. She began to drag the frightened dog back to the house. The wind was blowing harder now. Raylee heard something. *Is that a car?* she thought. She wasn't sure. When she reached the house, she saw Aunt Luelle's car. But Aunt Luelle was driving away. "No!" Raylee yelled, "Aunt Luelle! Wait!" But Aunt Luelle didn't hear her.

Aunt Luelle thinks I went with Momma, Raylee thought.

Storm Power

Raylee dragged Chomper into the house. "You're a bad dog," she said. Then she petted him. "I know you're frightened," she said gently. Raylee was frightened too. *What will I do now?* she wondered.

Raylee changed into dry clothes. Then she turned on the TV to watch the news. The news showed people in a shelter. Raylee looked for Momma and Aunt Luelle.

Raylee knew she needed water. She began to fill a bottle. Suddenly, she heard a SNAP! The lights went off. The TV went off. Raylee picked up the phone to call for help. She dialed 9-1-1. But the phone didn't work.

Water ran down the kitchen windows. Through the windows, Raylee could see the trees. They were bending in the wind. The storm was getting worse.

Well, thought Raylee, *I will have to ride out the storm. That is what Aunt Luelle always said —ride out the storm.* It means to keep safe until the storm is over. Raylee knew she had to do that all by herself.

Aunt Luelle had told Raylee stories about a bad hurricane. The hurricane was called Carla. Aunt Luelle said it was a very scary experience. "No one in the family should have to ride out a storm like that," she had said. *But Aunt Luelle left me to ride out the storm alone*, thought Raylee.

The wind was shrieking now. It was very strong. The walls shook. Water poured over the roof. Raylee sat in the living room. She had a flashlight and a bottle of water. Chomper lay at her feet. He looked up at her and cried.

Water and Wind

Raylee looked out the big living room window. There was a lot of water. The street looked like a river. The front yard looked like a lake. Raylee sat down again. BOOM! The wind blew out the living room window. Broken glass was all over the floor.

Chomper howled. Raylee grabbed him and went to the bathroom. The bathroom was a safe place. Raylee sat under the sink. She held Chomper close to her. The wind was still shrieking.

Suddenly there was a cracking sound. The front door was coming apart! Water was pouring into the house! It was coming into the bathroom!

Raylee jumped up. The water was at her ankles.
Then it was at her knees. The water was getting higher
and higher.

Raylee got out of the bathroom. She pushed
through the water into the hallway. There were chairs
and tables floating everywhere. She called to Chomper.
Together, Raylee and Chomper climbed the stairs to
the attic.

Raylee pulled down the attic door. She and Chomper sat at the edge of the attic opening. Just below them was the dark, dirty water. Raylee saw a dead fish. Pieces of wood and other debris floated in the water.

The attic was small, but it was dry. *I should not be in the attic*, thought Raylee. *An attic is a dangerous place to be during a hurricane.*

Aunt Luelle had told Raylee about a roof coming off during Hurricane Carla.

Roof, stay on! Raylee thought.

Riding It Out

Raylee leaned against a wall. Chomper sat beside her. The rain came down for hours. The rain on the roof made a sound like a thousand drummers.

Then suddenly it was quiet. *It's the eye of the storm,* thought Raylee. That was what the middle of the storm was called. That part of the storm was quiet for just a short time.

It was late afternoon. Raylee could see the sun shining on the water below. The water was high. It was halfway up the stairs. She could swim in the water. But it looked very dirty. *Maybe there are snakes in that water,* Raylee thought.

Soon it was not quiet anymore. The wind began to blow again. It was dark. The only light came from the flashlight. The rain pounded against the roof.

The roof shook harder and harder. Raylee prayed that the roof would not come off. She prayed that the wind would not blow her and Chomper into the dark night sky.

Through the Roof!

The hurricane lasted for many hours. Raylee and Chomper waited. Soon the flashlight went out. Raylee and Chomper waited in the dark. Raylee slept for a few minutes.

In the early morning Raylee woke up. She heard something. It was a helicopter. People were coming to rescue her. But how could Raylee let them know where she was?

Raylee looked up. She saw a vent. It was a small hole in the roof with a metal cover over it. Light was coming through the vent. Maybe she could crawl through the vent and wave at the helicopter. Raylee began to pull at the vent. It did not move. Raylee hit the vent with her flashlight. She hit the vent again and again. The cover began to move. In a few minutes, the cover came off.

Raylee had to make the hole bigger. She pounded at the wood to make a bigger hole.

"Here I am!" she yelled.

The people in the helicopter saw her! The helicopter came nearer to the house. Then a man was lowered from the helicopter. Soon Raylee and Chomper were safe.

Raylee had come through the hurricane. "I did it," she said. "I rode out the storm."